YIANNIS CHRISTOFIDES B.Sc., Ph.D.

The Orchids of Cyprus
A guide to the Cyprus orchids

To my mother

Published in Cyprus by the author
First edition 2001

Address: Minerva Hotel, 4820 Platres, Cyprus
Tel: +357-5-421731, Fax: +357-5-421075
E-mail: minerva@cylink.com.cy
http://www.cylink.com.cy/minerva/

All photographs are by the author

Cover page: *Orchis italica*
Back page: *Ophrys kotschyi*

ISBN 9963-8542-0-6

Graphic design Valentino Joseph
Printed in Cyprus by Lithostar

Preface

This book covers all the currently known Cyprus orchids as described in the Flora of Cyprus, except those not recorded for a number of years. Of these *Cephalanthera damasonium, Cephalanthera longifolia* and *Orchis papilionacea* are likely to be extinct in Cyprus. There is one report of *Orchis tridentata* (H. Jansen in Morschek Orchids of Cyprus) and unconfirmed reports of *Aceras anthropophorum,* and it is hoped that these orchids will be found again.

A brief description pointing out the main characteristics of each species is given, along with colour photographs. No precise locations are given of where to find orchids. Some are to be found everywhere, others are rare. For these, isolation is the only hope of survival.

It should not be necessary to be said but I will say it. Do not pick orchids or any other plant. It is illegal and damaging. I also urge you to be careful where you walk, and when taking photographs. Orchids are difficult to see when not in flower so do learn to recognise the rosettes so as not to tread on them.

Acknowledgements

My thanks are due to Gisella and Karlheinz Morschek for the many orchid-hunting trips, to Sallie and Rodney Bedford for the discovery of *Ophrys tenthredinifera*, and to Judy Dawes and Dr. F. Perring for comments on the manuscript.

Nomenclature

Specific names are given in italics, except when bold. Names following the species are those of the person/persons who described the plant. Also given are the common English and German names of the plant, if they exist, followed by the synonyms the plant may be encountered by in the literature.

Photography

The photographs in this book were taken with an Olympus OM1 35mm SLR camera fitted with an Olympus 50mm macro lens and a 25mm extension tube for close-ups. All photographs were taken using daylight on Kodachrome 100 ASA film at speeds of 1/60 sec or 1/30 sec. A tripod was used whenever possible.

The author

Yiannis Christofides was born in Platres, Cyprus and studied Chemistry at University College and Birkbeck College, London. He returned to Cyprus to run the family hotel in Platres and to take up botany.

Taxonomy

Orchids discussed in this book belong to the
following tribes within the Orchidaceae

Orchidaceae

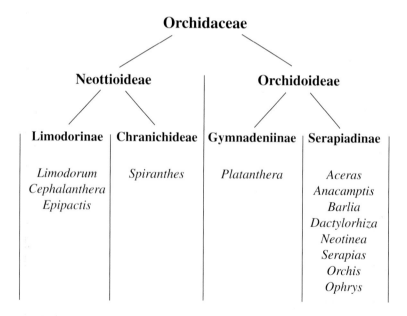

Neottioideae

Orchidoideae

Limodorinae	**Chranichideae**	**Gymnadeniinae**	**Serapiadinae**
Limodorum	*Spiranthes*	*Platanthera*	*Aceras*
Cephalanthera			*Anacamptis*
Epipactis			*Barlia*
			Dactylorhiza
			Neotinea
			Serapias
			Orchis
			Ophrys

Contents

Systematic list of species

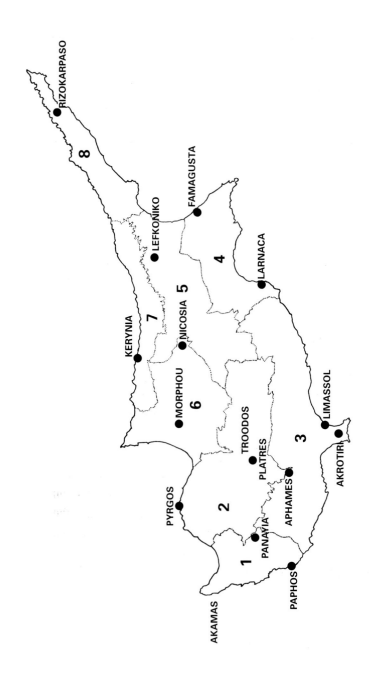

Botanical divisions of Cyprus according to Meikle

Topography

Cyprus is the result of the earth's tectonic activity. It is a piece of ophiolite (ocean crust) that has been uplifted as the African plate moved northwards and collided with the Eurasian plate. Originally the ophiolite was covered by a deep layer of sedimentary (calcareous) rock, which has been eroded from the upper part of the mountain to expose the igneous rock.

Cyprus consists of two mountain ranges, the Troodos and the Kyrenia. The Kyrenia range is composed of limestone and marbles, while the Troodos is predominantly igneous with chalk covering the lower slopes. In between lies the Mesaoria plain composed of sedimentary rocks (igneous, sands, gravels, chalk and gypsum).

A variety of habitats are found in lowland areas. The most important of these are maquis, garigue and the special habitats of the river valleys, the salt lakes and the marshes.

Garigue and maquis are terms used to describe the typical Mediterranean vegetation. Garigue is scrub-land with low growing shrubs such as *Thymus capitatus*, *Sarcopoterium spinosum* and *Cistus* species. Maquis is used to describe land with higher growing plants such as *Pistacia lentiscus*, *Olea europea*, *Ceratonia siliqua* (carob), *Genista sphacelata* and *Calycotome villosa*. Orchids such as *Neotinea maculata*, *Ophrys bornmuelleri*, *Ophrys levantina* and to a lesser extent *Ophrys fusca* and *Ophrys israelitica* are more shade tolerant and are to be found growing under the bigger shrubs.

Most other species prefer more open positions but all benefit from being in close proximity to larger shrubs and trees where there is less cultivation.

Meikle (Flora of Cyprus) subdivides the island into seven botanical divisions. Of these regions, 1 is the Akamas peninsula, 2 the igneous Troodos massif, 3 the lowland Paphos and Limassol areas and 4 the lowland Larnaka and Famagusta areas. Region 4 is mostly cultivated land. An interesting area to explore in region 4 is Cape Greco.

The Akamas peninsula in the north-west corner of Cyprus is an outcrop of the Troodos range consisting of a mixture of igneous and calcareous rocks. Here you will find deep limestone gorges with a variety of plants such as *Cyclamen cyprium, Centauria akamantis* and others not expected to be found in such a lowland area.

Region 2 consists of igneous rocks and can be separated into two areas with very different vegetation belts; the region from the coast to 1400 m and the sub-alpine region 1400-1960 m. In this higher region are found a large number of endemic plants, plus some interesting orchids such as *Limodorum abortivum, Cephalanthera rubra, Epipactis troodi, Epipactis condensata, Epipactis veratrifolia, Orchis anatolica, Orchis anatolica* ssp. *troodi* and *Platanthera chlorantha* ssp. *holmboei*.

The lower slopes of the Troodos massif are covered with *Pinus brutia* and extend from sea-level at the north-west coast (Pyrgos) to the foothills of Makhairas in central-eastern Cyprus. In the deeper shade of the Paphos forest you will find *Orchis syriaca, Orchis anatolica* ssp. *troodi,*

Akamas

Dactylorhiza romana, Limodorum abortivum, Platanthera chlorantha ssp. *holmboei, Epipactis troodi, Epipactis condensata, Barlia robertiana, Spiranthes spiralis.* In less forested areas you will also find *Ophrys mammosa, Ophrys israelitica* and *Serapias* species.

Region 3 consists of various heterogeneous areas. To the north is the Limassol forest area, an area of serpentine bounded by chalk. The chalk runs from Lefkara to the east through Aphames just south of Platres and Ayios Nicholaos to Panayia in the Paphos District. Here you will find most of the lowland orchids, including the rarer *Orchis punctulata* and *Orchis simia.*

Within region 3 the Akrotiri peninsula is a special area with a salt lake and the Phasouri reed beds. Here you will find many orchids including *Ophrys argolica* ssp. *elegans, Ophrys kotschyi* and *Orchis palustris. Orchis papilionacea* has been reported from this area (E. H. Sparrow, 1960) but has not been recorded recently.

Regions 5, 6, 7 and 8 which include the Kyrenia mountain range are inaccessible to Cypriots as the area is occupied by the Turkish army since the 1974 invasion.

Troodos

9

Orchid habitats

Garigue/Maquis Coastal areas to 1000 m

Orchis, all species. *Ophrys,* all species, *Dactylorhiza romana, Spiranthes spiralis, Anacamptis pyramidalis, Barlia robertiana* and *Neotinea maculata.*

Paphos forest

Orchis syriaca, Orchis anatolica ssp. *troodi, Dactylorhiza romana, Limodorum abortivum, Platanthera chlorantha* ssp. *holmboei, Epipactis troodi, Barlia robertiana, Spiranthes spiralis* and *Neotinea maculata.*

Troodos range

Streams: *Dactylorhiza iberica, Epipactis veratrifolia*
Woodland: *Limodorum abortivum, Cephalanthera rubra, Epipactis troodi, Epipactis condensata, Orchis anatolica, Orchis anatolica* ssp. *troodi, Platanthera chlorantha* ssp. *holmboei, Epipactis microphylla, Barlia robertiana, Dactylorhiza romana* and *Neotinea maculata.*

Wetlands

Lowland: *Orchis palustris, Orchis laxiflora.*
Troodos range: *Orchis laxiflora, Epipactis veratrifolia, Dactylorhiza iberica.*

Lowland habitat

Aphames

The orchid year

In Cyprus there is hardly a season when you cannot find an orchid in flower. The warm, rather dry winters, make for a much earlier season compared with the rest of the Mediterranean. The first orchids can be found in flower from the beginning of **January** near the Larnaka and Akrotiri salt lakes and the coastal strip between Limassol and Paphos. The earliest plants to flower are *Orchis collina* and *Barlia robertiana,* followed by *Ophrys argolica* ssp. *elegans, Ophrys flavomarginata* and *Ophrys sintenisii.*

These continue to flower during **February** and are followed by the rest of the *Ophrys fusca* complex, *Orchis syriaca, Orchis punctulata* and *Orchis quadripunctata.*

During **March** orchids higher up in the hills start to flower. You should be able to find *Orchis anatolica* ssp. *troodi, Orchis quadripunctata, Ophrys mammosa, Dactylorhiza romana* and *Barlia robertiana* in flower at altitudes of 1000 m. By this time the later flowering orchids, such as *Orchis coriophora* ssp. *fragrans, Orchis sancta, Anacamptis pyramidalis, Ophrys apifera, Ophrys bornmuelleri* and *Serapias* are starting to flower near the coast.

By **April** the plains have started to dry out and the only places to find orchids are the hills. During **April** and **May** look at the limit of the chalk hills in the Limassol and Paphos Districts, the top of the river valleys of the Xeros and the Dhiarizos. The lowland season is extended into May by *Orchis palustris,* found in marshy areas.

A little later in **June** *Dactylorhiza iberica* starts flowering in the streams high in the Troodos range and in the pine forest you will find the saprophytic *Limodorum abortivum*. *Epipactis* spp. start flowering with *E. troodi*, followed by *E. veratrifolia*, and *E. microphylla*.

Later in **July** *Cephalanthera rubra* is to be found in flower in the deep shade of *Pinus nigra* forest as is E*pipactis condensata*. The season is completed with the late autumn flowering orchid *Spiranthes spiralis* in **November/ December**, to be found under pines in lowland areas up to 900 m.

The orchid family

Orchids are one of the most widespread families of plants. They are found in very diverse environments, from the tropics to near the Arctic circle. Despite their ability to have adapted to such very different environments, they are plants which require stable environmental conditions. Some orchids require up to 10 years to reach flowering stage and if at any time the environment is disturbed, the whole process is halted.

Orchids belong to the plants with one cotyledon and net-veined leaves (Monocotyledonae). They share other attributes of this subclass, like scattered vascular bundles, parallel leaf venation, flower parts in threes and inferior ovary. It is convenient to divide the family into two groups, the terrestrial species and the epiphytic, although the division is not clear cut and a number of terrestrial species are found in groups that are primarily epiphytic. The orchids that grow in Cyprus are wholly terrestrial.

In evolutionary terms the orchid family is related to the lily family. Both have six perianth segments (the sepals and petals or tepals), although in the orchid family they tend to be highly differentiated. In fact it is this differentiation of some of the tepals which distinguishes one orchid from another. In some genera, such as *Ophrys*, one of the tepals, the lip, has developed in such a way as to mimic the appearance of an insect such a bee or a fly. This appears to be a mechanism for achieving cross-pollination between plants of the same species.

Naming orchids

The scientific name of a species consists of the generic name, e.g. *Anacamptis*, followed by the specific name e.g. *pyramidalis*. Closely related species are placed in the same genus and share the same generic name. The decision to place a species in a specific genus is usually based on morphological criteria. Sometimes, because of better understanding of the relationships between species, it has been necessary to change the genus a plant is placed in, and hence to change its generic name. The specific name stays the same. A case in point is *Anacamptis pyramidalis*, which was placed in different genera by different workers, and was previously described as *Orchis pyramidalis* (1753) or *Aceras pyramidalis* (1851).

More recently, the advent of molecular genetic techniques has thrown a different light on the relationships between various genera. A case in point are the *Anacamptis*, *Orchis*, *Aceras* and *Neotinea* genera, which are discussed in the chapter describing *Orchis*.

The orchid flower

The orchid inflorescence is usually racemose, with the flowers axillary on the rachis and usually flowering from the base upward - 3 exceptions in the Mediterranean area one, *Orchis simia*, found in Cyprus.

The orchid flower shows bilateral symmetry, that is one can draw one, and only one, line down the middle of the flower; the two parts will then be mirror images. The special characteristics of the orchid flower are summarized below:

1. Flower parts come in threes. Three sepals or outer segments and three petals or inner segments. The median petal is virtually always differentiated from the other two and is called the lip.

2. The stamens are all on one side of the flower, rather than being symmetrically arranged. Most orchids have only one fertile stamen (one genus has three).

3. The stamen and the pistil (the female part) are partly or completely united into a single structure called the column.

4. The flower usually twists around in the course of development. This a process called resurpination.

5. The pollen is usually bound together in a few large masses (pollinia), a feature which is intimately involved in the pollination by insects.

Epipactis condensata

Limodorum abortivum

Orchis anatolica ssp. *troodi*

Ophrys lutea ssp. *galilaea*

The species

Since the sixteenth century naturalists have tried to find a scientific definition of the term species. The English naturalist John Ray (1627-1705) raised the question in a discourse given to the Royal Society on 17 December 1674. He discusses what constitutes a species and the question of intraspecific variation where individuals differ from the normal in height, scent, flower colour, multiplicity of leaves and variegation. Charles Darwin concludes that given the endless variability seen in nature, 'Certainly no clear line of demarcation has as yet been drawn between species and subspecies. The problem arises because evolution is an ongoing process and in a rapidly changing environment new variants take the place of the original organism'. Darwin recognises both the transitory nature of the species and also the subjective element in the recognition.

There are two meanings that we can attach to the word species. One is the taxonomist's unit, used for a descriptive classification. The biologists view is of 'species as a unit composed of individuals which are able to interbreed with a high level of freedom under a specified set of conditions and separated by other species by at least partial sterility', or 'a population of actually or potentially interbreeding organisms sharing a common gene pool'.
Although the above definitions may sound precise, just consider what is meant by 'potentially interbreeding organisms'. I shall examine this question later.

And what of the subspecies? In 'Systematics and the origin of the Species' Ernst Mayr (1942) says: The subspecies or geographic race is a geographically and taxonomically localised subdivision of the species, which differs genetically and taxonomically from other subdivisions of the species'. We need to satisfy two criteria:

1. Subspecies must be recognisable by features of their morphology, physiology or behaviour; that is they must be taxonomically different from other subspecies.

2. A subspecies must occupy a subdivision of the total geographic range of the species. The subspecies differs from the species in that its boundaries can never be fixed and definite because by definition a member of one subspecies can interbreed with members of any other subspecies in its species. A group that cannot breed with others closely related forms must be designated a full species.

You might think that by applying the above definitions we would arrive at satisfactory classifications; however this is not always the case. We need to look at the definition more closely and even then nature will defeat us, because we are attempting to describe something which is dynamic and variable in a static and fixed frame. The terms 'interbreeding' or 'potentially interbreeding' used to define a species need to be examined. What are the important isolating mechanisms separating species?

1. Species found in the same region occur in different habitats.
2. Species found in the same habitat flower at different times.
3. Species use different pollinators.
4. Fertilization may take place but F1 hybrids or latter generations are not viable.

How do species arise?

The most important mode of speciation is 'gradual speciation'. That is, individuals in a geographical area are subjected to selection pressures leading to plants with a different gene pool compared to the parents. Eventually sufficient genetic diversification will occur, so that when the two daughter species are brought together they are prevented from crossing freely.

However the reverse is also true: morphological diversification is possible without any appreciable loss in sterility. This is a much more common occurrence in nature than people think and is not confined to the Orchids.

The case of the subgenus *Geum* illustrates the point. All twenty-five species in the genus will hybridise with each other and most of the hybrids are at least partially fertile; under our definition all twenty-five should be placed in a single species. In practice, however, hybridisation will not take place under natural conditions.

And that, I think should be the guiding light when attempting to decide what is and what is not a species. The question of the status of the Cyprus orchids will be discussed for each one individually.

Why so many orchid species?

Genetic isolation of species will lead, in different environments, to selective pressures on populations. Orchids are highly prolific, producing millions of seeds and showing a high degree of response to environmental pressures. Individuals colonising new sites are more likely to show new characteristics, as they are no longer constrained by the gene pool of larger populations. So homozygous characters can establish themselves within a couple of generations, something unlikely in a larger population.

Cyprus has been isolated from the nearby Eurasian land mass ever since the Mediterranean filled up, about six million years ago. Even before this event, the Eastern Mediterranean was sufficiently isolated from the mainland for speciation to occur. A number of species are confined either to Cyprus or the wider Levant area.

The orchids to be found exclusively in Cyprus are: *Orchis troodi, Ophrys kotschyi* and *Ophrys lapethica*.

Other orchids to be found in the wider Levant area are:
Orchis coriophora ssp. *fragrans, Orchis punctulata, Orchis sancta, Orchis syriaca, Ophrys umbilicata, Ophrys bornmuelleri, Ophrys levantina, Ophrys israelitica, Ophrys argolica* ssp. *elegans, Ophrys transhyrcana, Ophrys lutea* ssp. *galilaea, Ophrys sintenisii, Platanthera chlorantha* ssp. *holmboei, Epipactis troodi, Epipactis condensata, Epipactis veratrifolia* and *Dactylorhiza iberica*.

Hybrids

The occurrence of hybridisation in natural populations is not common. If you spend a season studying orchids you are likely to come across only one or two hybrids. Before reaching the conclusion that the plant is a hybrid you need to consider whether a large number of characters are intermediate between the parent species, and not to rely on just one. You also need to check that both parents are growing in the vicinity and are flowering.

The following hybrids have been recorded:

Anacamptis pyramidalis x *Orchis coriophora* ssp. *fragrans*
Orchis coriophora ssp. *fragrans* x *Orchis sancta*
Ophrys lutea ssp. *galilaea* x *Ophrys sintenisii*
Ophrys mammosa x *Ophrys kotschyi*

Ophrys lutea ssp. *galilaea* x *Ophrys sintenisii*

Ophrys kotschyi x *Ophrys mammosa*

Ophrys levantina x *Ophrys flavomarginata*

23

Orchis sancta x *Orchis coriophora* ssp. *fragrans*

Anacamptis pyramidalis x *Orchis coriophora* ssp. *fragrans*

Flower abnormalities

Orchid flowers can show two types of abnormalities. One is colour variability and the other structural variability.

Colour abnormalities are the result of lack of anthocyanins (hypochromy) the pigments that give flowers their colouration. Flowers lacking in colour pigments are white (*Orchis* and related genera) or yellow (*Ophrys*). Sometimes hypochromy can affect part of the flower such as the lip as can be seen in *Ophrys mammosa* var. *planimaculata.*

Flower abnormality can manifest itself in several ways such as three lip-shaped petals, or a lip divided into two.

Ophrys lutea ssp. *galilaea*

Ophrys kotschyi

Ophrys iricolor

Ophrys bornmuelleri

Orchis italica

Orchis syriaca

Orchis anatolica ssp. *troodi*

Ophrys mammosa var. *planimaculata*

THE ORCHIDS

Ophrys apifera var. *bicolor*

Limodorum abortivum *(L.) Swartz*

Violet Limodore, Violetter Dingel

If there is an exotic looking orchid amongst the Cyprus orchids then this it. With the individual flowers reaching 4 cm across, and the plant growing to 75 cm tall, this is certainly one of the tallest orchids on Cyprus.

It grows in association with *Pinus brutia* and *Pinus nigra* and is probably dependent on these trees. It is the only saprophytic orchid that we have here and it obtains its nutrients in a similar way to a fungus, as it has no green leaves of its own. The plant lives underground until it has enough energy to flower, when it pushes its flower spike above the ground. I have counted up to twelve spikes growing closely together, probably from the same plant. When I have looked for them in subsequent years I have not found any in the same location, only the remains of last years flower spikes. It would appear that sometimes the plants flower themselves to death. Flower colour is usually lilac, except for very rare white specimens.

Flowering time: May-June

Habitat: pine forest 200-1500 m

Occurrence: locally common.

Cephalanthera rubra *(L.) L. C. M. Richard*

Red Helleborine, Rotes Waldvögelein

Plant 20-40 cm tall, flowers pale to deep pink. One of the few plants that thrives in the deep shade of the *Pinus nigra* forest of the high Troodos. The pink flowers open in late June-July, at the same time as *Epilobium angustifolium,* which also grows in the same habitat.

Two other *Cephalanthera* species, *C. damasonium* and *C. longifolia* were recorded a long time ago (by Kotschy and Sundermann respectively) but have not been collected since and are unlikely to be found on the island.

Flowering time:
late June-July

Habitat:
Pinus nigra forest in deep
shade, 1400-1600 m

Occurrence:
rare but locally common.

A genus of about 30 species distributed in Europe and Asia. In Cyprus they are represented by four species. A fifth species, *E. helleborine,* has been found once and is probably extinct.

Epipactis veratrifolia *Boissier et Hohenacker*

Eastern Marsh Helleborine, Germerblättrige Stendelwurz

Plant to one metre tall, robust. Leaves 10-20 cm long. Flowers large ca. 30 mm in diameter.

Flowering time:
June-August (March-May at Episkopi)

Habitat:
streams and river beds on the higher slopes of Troodos, 800-1500 m One lowland site on a wet cliff at Episkopi

Occurrence:
locally common.

Epipactis troodi *Lindberg*

Cyprus Helleborine

Leaves ovate, glabrous, dark green stained purple-violet.
Inflorescence lax, few flowered. Sepals glabrous.

Flowering time:
June-July

Habitat:
pine forest,
800-1800 m

Occurrence:
locally common.

Epipactis microphylla *(Ehrhardt) Swartz*

Small-leafed Helleborine, Kleinblättrige Stendelwurz

Plant slender to 30 cm tall. Flowers small, few, greenish-white. Sepals pubescent on the outside.

Flowering time:
middle to late June

Habitat:
in deep shade in
forests, 600-800 m

Occurrence:
rare.

Epipactis condensata *Boiss. ex D. P. Young*

Dense-flowered Helleborine, Dichtblütige Stendelwurz

Plant robust, to 70 cm high, several stems growing together. Sepals green, pubescent. Flowers many, closely spaced. Inner surface of hypochile dark violet.

Flowering time:
July

Habitat:
open pine forest,
1500-1700 m

Occurrence:
rare.

Spiranthes spiralis *(L.) Chevallier*

Autumn Lady's Tresses, Herbst-Drehwurz

An orchid with a different life cycle from the others. The rosette that appears in the winter does not flower the following spring as do other orchids, but dies down in the summer and the flower is produced at the onset of the autumn rains. The new rosette appears later in December alongside the flower spike.

The orchid takes its name from the way the little white flowers spiral around the stem, sometimes producing as many as three spirals. The orchid is found in pine forests from the Akamas to the valleys in the Paphos forest.

Flowering time:
November-December

Habitat:
pine forest, on a variety
of soil, 0-800 m

Occurrence:
locally common.

Platanthera chlorantha ssp. holmboei
(Lindberg f.) J. J. Wood

Holmboe's Butterfly Orchid
Platanthera holmboei H. Lindberg fil.

A mountain orchid, growing in pine forests. Flowers greenish-white. Meikle recognises two subspecies growing in Cyprus; the nominate race ssp. *chlorantha* and ssp. *holmboei*. The differences between the two are minimal and rest on flower colour (whitish for ssp. *chlorantha* and entirely green for ssp. *holmboei*) and small differences on sepal and lip size and shape. It appears that of the records of specimens found on Cyprus all but two are of ssp. *holmboei*.

Flowering time:
May-June

Habitat:
pine forest, 800-1600 m

Occurrence:
locally common.

44

Aceras anthropophorum *(L.) R. Brown*

Man Orchid, Ohnsporn

One records exists of this species, that of Kotschy in 1859 "between Omodhos and Limassol, near Ayios Tharapon". Despite considerable searching it has not been possible to locate this orchid. It should be looked for in the Ayios Therapon-Ayios Ambrosios areas (Limassol District) in late March/April.

Inflorescence cylindrical, flowers greenish-yellow with red/brown edge. Sepals form hood. Can easily be distinguished from *Orchis* species as the flower has no spur.

Flowering time: late March-April

Habitat: garigue, short grassland

Occurrence: extinct?

Anacamptis pyramidalis

Anacamptis pyramidalis *(L.) L. C. M. Richard*

Pyramidal Orchid, Pyramidenorchis

A late flowering orchid, it can be found from almost at sea level on the edge of the Akrotiri salt lake to ca. 1000 m in open pine forest. Flower colour ranges from pure white (rare), pale pink to darker shades of pink. It can be readily distinguished from other orchids by the two small ridges found on the base of the lip.

Flowering time: late March-April-May

Habitat: garigue, roadside, open pine forest, 0-1000 m

Occurrence: locally common.

48

Barlia robertiana *(Loiseleur) Greuter*

Giant Orchid, Roberts Knabenkraut

An early flowering orchid, sometimes to be found flowering by the end of December. Because its range extends to ca. 1200 m (Platres) it can be found in flower as late as April. *Barlia robertiana* is an imposing orchid reaching 70 cm in height. Flower colour is variable ranging from greenish-white to deep pink.

Flowering time: January-April

Habitat: garigue, short grassland, 0-1200 m

Occurrence: common.

50

Dactylorhiza iberica *(M. Bieb. ex Willd.) Soó*

Crimean Orchid,   Krim-Knabenkraut

One of the two *Dactylorhiza* species to be found on Cyprus. This species grows by streams and in wet places in the Troodos range, 1000-1600 m. It is to be found in flower later in the year, June-July. Flowers pink, labellum spotted dark purple.

Flowering time:
June-July

Habitat:
streams and damp places,
1000-1600 m

Occurrence:
rare, because of habitat.

Dactylorhiza romana *(Sebastiani) Soó*

Roman Orchid, Römisches Knabenkraut

D. sulphurea ssp. *pseudosambucina* (Ten.) Franco
D. sambucina ssp. *pseudosambucina* (Ten.) Sundermann

Dactylorhiza romana comes in two colour variations, a pink and a yellow form. In Cyprus however only the yellow-flowered variety exists. It is found in pine forest in the Akamas, the Paphos and Troodos range.

Flowering time:
March-April

Habitat:
pine forest, 0-1000 m

Occurrence:
locally common.

Neotinea maculata *(Desfontaines) Stearn*

Dense-flowered Orchid, Gefleckte Waldwurz

Neotinea maculata is to be found growing in deep shade under shrubs or on north facing hillsides which are moist throughout the winter. Its small flowers are packed closely on the stem and the whole plant rarely grows taller than 15 cm. The flowers are usually pink/white or more rarely, pure white.

Flowering time:
March-May

Habitat:
often under cover,
100-1500 m

Occurrence:
locally common.

SERAPIAS

Serapias laxiflora

The genus *Serapias* is basically a Mediterranean genus, also found in the Caucasus. The closest relatives to the genus are *Anacamptis* and *Orchis* and hybrids are recorded with both, especially with *O. syriaca, O. coriophora* and *O. papilionacea.* It is a genus that is undergoing active speciation, especially in the Eastern Mediterranean.

In Cyprus three subspecies are recognised by J. J. Wood (Meikle), *S. vomeracea* ssp. *vomeracea, S. vomeracea* ssp. *laxiflora* and *S. vomeracea* ssp. *orientalis.* In addition to these *S. parviflora* has also been recorded here (Morschek).

Delforge proposes a new rare endemic species for Cyprus, *S. aphroditae,* confined to the Akamas peninsula and similar to *S. parviflora.* Another species, *S. levantina* intermediate between *S. orientalis* and *S. vomeracea* is also recorded from Cyprus. The status of these plants needs to be evaluated.

To differentiate between the species you need to consider the following characters:

1. Plant height and arrangement of the inflorescence

2. Floral bract and galea length

3. Shape and length of the lip.

Serapias vomeracea *(N. L. Burman) Briquet*

Plough-share Serapias, Pflugschar-Zungenstendel
Serapias vomeracea ssp. *vomeracea*

Plant tall, up to 60 cm high; inflorescence lax, galea 20-30 mm long, floral bracts greatly exceeding galea, lip 20-40 mm long.

Flowering time:
late March-May

Habitat:
garigue, fields with
grass, 0-1000 m

Occurrence:
rare

Serapias laxiflora *Chaub.*

Lockerblütiger Zungenstendel
Serapias bergonii *E. G. Camus*
Serapias vomeracea ssp. *laxiflora* (Soó) Gölz et Reinhard

Plant short, 15-30 cm high,, inflorescence lax, galea 15-20 cm long, floral bracts equal to or slightly exceeding the galea, lip 15-30 mm long.

Flowering time:
late March-May

Habitat:
garigue, fields with
grass, 0-1100 m

Occurrence:
common

61

Serapias orientalis *(W. Greuter) Baumann et Künkele*

Eastern Serapias, Orientalischer Zungenstendel
Serapias vomeracea ssp. *orientalis* Greuter

Plant short 10-25 cm high, inflorescence dense, floral
bracts equal or shorter than the galea, lip 20-30 mm long.

Flowering time:
March

Habitat:
garigue, fields with
grass, 0-150 m

Occurrence:
rare, locally
common

Serapias parviflora *Parlatore*

Small-flowered Serapias, Kleinblütiger Zungenstendel

Plant 15-40 cm high, floral bracts equal to galea, lip short
12-20 mm long. Characterised by cleistogamous flowers;
the pod will have started developing by the time the flowers
have opened.

Flowering time:
late March-April

Habitat:
garigue, fields with
grass, 0-600 m

Occurrence:
rare

Serapias levantina *H. Baumann et Künkele*

A species intermediate in character between *S. orientalis* and *S. laxiflora*. The photo was taken at Akrotiri, where both these species have been recorded. Whether *S. levantina* is indeed a new species or a hybrid between the other two remains to be seen.

Flowering time:
late March-April

Habitat:
garigue, fields with
grass, 0-150 m

Occurrence:
rare

ORCHIS

Orchis punctulata

The *Aceras, Anacamptis, Neotinea* and *Orchis* genera are to be found in Europe, North Africa and Asia as far as Japan. Within *Orchis,* a number of species can be placed together in groups of related orchids, based on the length and shape of the petals and sepals. The closeness of the species within these groupings is further evidenced by the frequency of hybridisation within these groupings, compared to members of other groupings. What is also evident is that certain *Orchis* species (e.g. *Orchis coriophora* ssp. *fragrans)* hybridise more readily with species in other genera, in this case *Anacamptis,* rather than with members of the *Orchis* genus.

The work of Bateman et al, who sequenced the nuclear ribosomal DNA internal transcribed spaces ITS1 and ITS2, (discussion outside the scope of this book but see references) has revealed closer relationships between certain groupings within the *Orchis* genus with *Anacamptis* or *Neotinea.* These orchids (with chromosome numbers 2n=36, or 2n=32) are transferred to *Anacamptis, Orchis tridentata* is transferred to *Neotinea* and *Aceras* is placed within *Orchis.*

I have retained the use of the established names for these orchids, but readers should be aware that the new names will become commonplace.

Current groups	New proposal*
Laxiflora group	
Orchis laxiflora	*Anacamptis laxiflora*
Orchis palustris	*Anacamptis palustris*
Coriophora group	
Orchis coriophora	*Anacamptis coriophora*
Orchis sancta	*Anacamptis sancta*
Collina group	
Orchis collina	*Anacamptis collina*
Papilionacea group	
Orchis papilionacea	*Anacamptis papilionacea*
(Anacamptis pyramidalis)	*Anacamptis pyramidalis*
Morio group	
Orchis syriaca	*Anacamptis syriaca*
Quadripuncata group	
Orchis quadripuncata	*Orchis quadripuncata*
Mascula group	
Orchis anatolica	*Orchis anatolica*
Orchis anatolica ssp. *troodi*	*Orchis anatolica* ssp. *troodi*
Militaris group	
Orchis punctulata	*Orchis punctulata*
Orchis italica	*Orchis italica*
Orchis simia	*Orchis simia*
(Aceras anthropophorum)	*Orchis anthropophorum*
Orchis tridentata	*Neotinea tridentata*
(Neotinea maculata)	*Neotinea maculata*

* Bateman et al, see references

Meikle assigns specific status to these two orchids. In Cyprus at least, they are not found to grow together and no hybrids have been found. *O. laxiflora* flowers earlier than *O. palustris*, which minimises any potential inbreeding. The specific status assigned to this pair is therefore justified.

Orchis laxiflora *Lamarck*

Loose-flowered Orchid, Lockerblutiges Knabenkraut
O. laxiflora ssp. *laxiflora*

Plant to 80 cm tall. Flowers deep violet-purple, lip with white central area, not spotted. Lip three lobed, middle lobe shorter than side lobes, the latter usually turned down.

Flowering time:
late March-May

Habitat:
marshes, river beds,
wet hillsides, 0-800 m

Occurrence:
rare but locally common.

Orchis palustris *Jacquin*

Lax-flowered Orchid, Sumpfkabenkraut
O. laxiflora Lam. ssp. *palustris* Jacquin

Plant to 80 cm tall. Flowers pink to dark purple, central area white flecked purple. Lip three lobed, middle lobe longer than the side lobes which are spread flat.

Flowering times:
late April-May

Habitat:
lowland marshes,
sometimes in quite tall
grass or reeds

Occurrence:
very rare now and will
probably be extinct soon
because of drainage of
marshes.

O. coriophora ssp. *fragrans*
O. sancta

Orchis coriophora ssp. *fragrans* and *Orchis sancta* are two closely related, late flowering orchids. On the edge of the Akrotiri salt lake these orchids start flowering towards the end of March and they may be found still flowering on the hillsides until the middle of May. The two orchids are often found growing together and you come across the occasional hybrid.

Orchis coriophora ssp. fragrans *(Pollini) Camus*

Bug Orchid, Wanzenknabenkraut
O. fragrans Pollini

Flowers scented, spotted in the centre of the lip. Lip three-lobed, lobes turned down. Lip colour variable from white flecked with green to dark red spots, to dark red.

Flowering time: late March- May

Habitat: garigue, short grassland on sedimentary or calcareous soils, roadside, 0-1400 m

Occurrence: common.

Orchis sancta *L.*

Holy Orchid, Heiliges Knabenkraut

The Holy Orchid, so named because of the hood formed by the sepals and petals. Flowers pale pink to reddish-pink, unscented, uniformly coloured, never spotted. Lip three lobed, lobes flat or curving upward.

Flowering time; late March-May

Habitat: garigue, calcareous or igneous soils, 0-1000 m

Occurrence: locally common but rarer than *Orchis coriophora* ssp. *fragrans.*

Orchis collina *Banks et Solander*

Fan-lipped Orchid, Hugelknabenkraut
Orchis saccata

Orchis collina starts flowering at the beginning of January, one of the first orchids to do so. It is to be found in coastal areas and inland up to 1000 m. The plant grows up to 30 cm tall; flowers variable in colour, from greenish-white to purple, not spotted.

Flowering time:
January-March

Habitat:
garigue, 0-1000 m

Occurrence:
common or locally common.

Spur elongate, filiform, downward pointing.

Orchis quadripunctata *Cyrillo ex Tenore*

Four-spotted Orchid, Vierpunktknabenkraut

Flower colour ranges from pure white (usually) to pink. Lip spotted, 3-7 spots. The height of the plant varies from 5 to 25 cm, depending on where it grows. At first glance it resembles *O. anatolica* or *O. anatolica* ssp. *troodi.* It can be separated easily from the other two because for *O. quadripuncata* the spur points downward, whereas for *O. anatolica* the spur is horizontal and for *O. anatolica* ssp. *troodi* the spur curves upward.

Flowering time:
February-March-April

Habitat:
poor igneous rocks and
chalk, 0-1000 m

Occurrence:
locally common.

Orchis anatolica. Spur in horizontal position
Orchis anatolica ssp. *troodi.* Spur points upward

J. J. Wood(Meikle) assigns varietal status to *O. a. troodi,* whereas other workers assign sub-specific or even specific status (*O. troodi*). *O. anatolica* in Cyprus is found on the Kerynia range and on the lower eastern and northern slopes of the Troodos range. *O. anatolica* ssp. *troodi* is found higher on Troodos and on the Akamas.

Orchis anatolica ssp. troodi *(Renz) Soó*

Anatolian Orchid ssp. troodi
Anatolisches Knabenkraut ssp. troodi
Orchis troodi *(Renz) Delforge*

The special *Orchis* of the Troodos range found in the Paphos and Troodos forests up to an altitude of 1500 m and in the Akamas. It grows in light to dense woodland and can reach a height of 30 cm. Leaves spotted. Flower colour white to deep pink, lip spotted. Lateral sepals upward pointing. Spur always points upward, describing a semicircle.

Flowering time: March-April-May

Habitat: pine forest, shade to semi-shade, 100-1500 m

Occurrence: locally common. Akamas, Mesapotamos, Paphos forest, Platres,, Prodromos, Trooditissa, Platys river valley.

Orchis anatolica *Boissier*

Anatolian Orchid
Anatolisches Knabenkraut

As for *Orchis anatolica* ssp. *troodi* but spur in horizontal position.

Flowering time: Feb. - March

Habitat: pine forest, shade to semi-shade, 100-500 m

Occurrence:lower northern and eastern slopes of the Troodos range and on the Kyrenia range.

Orchis syriaca *Boisser ex H. Baumann et Künkele*

Green-winged Orchid, Syrisches Knabenkraut
Orchis morio ssp. *syriaca* E. G. Camus
Orchis morio L. ssp. *libani* Renz

Probably the commonest orchid in Cyprus, growing in profusion in some areas. It has a fairly long flowering period from early February to April. It is to be found growing equally on chalk and igneous soils, from the coast to 1000 m.

The plant grows from a few cm (in times of drought) to up to 20 cm high. The lip is entire to shortly trilobed and ranges in colour from pure white to deep pink, always without spots. The orchid can always be recognised by the green veining of the sepals forming the hood.

J. J. Wood (Meikle) presents a rather complicated picture of *O. morio* in Cyprus suggesting the presence of two varieties, var. *picta* and var. *libani*. Var. *picta* should have a distinctly three-lobed lip, with dark pink to pale purple spots whereas for var. *libani* the lip is sub-entire with no spotting. In fact no specimens are ever found with spots on the lip suggesting the presence in Cyprus of only one type.

Flowering time: February-April

Habitat: garigue, calcareous or igneous soils, 0-1000 m

Occurrence: common.

85

Orchis tridentata
Orchis italica: leaves wavy along edges
Orchis simia: leaves straight edged,
flowers open from the top
Orchis punctulata: flowers yellow.

Orchis tridentata *Scopoli*

Toothed Orchid, Dreizahniges knabenkraut

Sepals pink-purplish, lip three-lobed. One recent record of this plant (Hansen in Morschek p.164) but none have been found since then. Should be looked for in the Kyvides and Lefkara areas in late March.

Orchis italica *Poiret*

Naked-man Orchid, Italienisches Knabenkraut

A field of *Orchis italica* is a sight to behold. It is an early coloniser on sites that have recently been destroyed by fire. The flowers range in colour from pale pink to lilac with the sepals having darker-coloured veins. White specimens are very rare. *Orchis italica* has distinct wavy-edged leaves, often spotted, so the plant can always be identified even before the flower is open.

Flowering time: March-early April

Habitat: garigue, cleared hillsides

Occurrence: locally common, 0-900 m.

Orchis italica

Orchis simia *Lamarck*

Monkey Orchid, Affenknabenkraut

One of the most beautiful of the Cyprus orchids. The flower is white except for the tips of the "arms and legs" of the lip, which are a beautiful purple. The lip is usually white with tufts of purple papillae. The individual flowers start opening at the top of the inflorescence in contrast to all other Cyprus orchids. Leaves are unspotted and straight edged. *Orchis simia* may be found in a narrow band of chalk hills 600-800 m in the Limassol District. In some years it can be found in profusion but if the rains fail then populations can collapse.

Flowering time:
March-April

Habitat:
dry chalk hills, under pine, 600-800 m

Occurrence:
rare, locally common.

Orchis punctulata *Steven ex Lindley*

Punctate Orchid, Punktiertes Knabenkraut

One of the rarer species of the *Orchis* genus. It grows in several isolated areas on the island e.g. the Akamas, coastal areas around Paphos and Limassol and inland in the Larnaka District.

Flowering time:
February-March

Habitat:
garigue, in quite
dense vegetation,
0-600 m

Occurrence:
rare, locally
common.

OPHRYS

Ophrys lutea ssp. *galilaea*

Introduction

Essentially a Mediterranean genus with a few species straying into Northern Europe. The lip of the flower bears a remarkable resemblance to an insect and indeed it is part of the deception of the flower to induce the insect to think it is the female of the species and to copulate with it thus effecting cross-fertilisation. The flower also produces a scent resembling the female sex hormone further adding to the deception. Orchids within the *Ophrys* genus have co-evolved with their own pollinators, each species producing stimuli specific to one species of pollinator so ensuring that cross-fertilisation is kept within members of same species.

The *Ophrys* genus presents the researcher with considerable problems in taxonomy. Should the subspecies of the *O. fusca, O. bornmuelleri, O. umbilicata* and *O. sphegodes* groups, be given specific status or not? Given that in Cyprus all species grow within the same geographical area and they do not hybridise, it is now accepted that they be given specific status.

General characteristics

Leaves basal and/or cauline, unspotted; 3 outer sepals larger, 2 inner petals smaller; labellum without a spur, entire or 3-lobed, often convex, with 2 lateral protuberances at the base or 2 small swellings.

To recognise the different species you must consider the following:

Colour of sepals-green/white/pink
Colour of petals-green/white/pink
Size of petals relative to sepals
Is the median sepal curved back or forward over the gynostegium?
Is the lip entire or trilobed?
Are the edges turned up or down?
Is there a narrow or broad yellow edge to the lip?
Are there obvious humps on the lip?
Is there a V-shaped depression at the bottom of the lip?

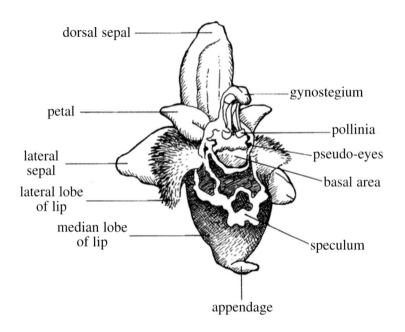

dorsal sepal

gynostegium

petal

pollinia

lateral
sepal

pseudo-eyes

basal area

lateral lobe
of lip

median lobe
of lip

speculum

appendage

An *Ophrys* flower

94

Ophrys kotchyi

Ophrys fusca/lutea group
O. fusca (O. funera)
O. iricolor
O. lutea ssp. *galilaea*

Ophrys omegaifera group
O. israelitica (O. fusca ssp. *fleischmannii)*

Ophrys bornmuelleri group
O. bornmuelleri, O. levantina

Ophrys tenthredinifera group
O. tenthredinifera

Ophrys apifera group
O. apifera

Ophrys argolica group
O. argolica ssp. *elegans (O. elegans)*

Ophrys scolopax group
O. rhodia

Ophrys umbilicata group
O. kotschyi, O. lapethica
O. umbilicata, O. attica, O. flavomarginata

Ophrys mammosa / sphegodes group
O. mammosa, O. transhyrcana, O. sintenisii

O. fusca (*O. funera*)
O. iricolor
O. lutea ssp. *galilaea*

The *Ophrys fusca/lutea* group is distributed in the Mediterranean basin and is represented by 20 or so species or subspecies. Some authors treat most of the variants as subspecies of one of the species belonging to the three main groups (*O. fusca, O. iricolor* and *O. lutea*). Others (Delforge) treat the subspecies within the main groupings as species in their own right.

In Cyprus the situation is fairly simple, with each group being represented by a single species. Three species are thus recognised. *Ophrys fusca* (*O. fusca* ssp. *fusca*), *Ophrys iricolor* (*O. fusca* ssp. *iricolor*) and *Ophrys lutea* ssp. *galilaea*.

Ophrys israelitica (*Ophrys fusca* ssp. *fleischmannii*) is placed outside the group for reasons of morphology. Whereas all the other members share the feature of indentation at the base of the lip, *Ophrys israelitica* lacks this and is considered part of the Omegaifera group.

Ophrys fusca *Link*

Dull Ophrys, Rotbraune Ragwurz
O. fusca Link ssp. *fusca*
O. fusca ssp. *funerea* (Viviani) Archaengeli vel Nyman
O. funerea *(Viviani) E. G. et A. Camus et Bergon*

Most authors use the name *O. fusca* to describe the plant found in Cyprus, whereas Delforge reserves the name *O. fusca* for the larger-flowered plants found elsewhere in the Mediterranean and uses the name *O. funerea* for the smaller-flowered taxon found in Cyprus and elsewhere. Whichever name one uses for the Cypriot plant the fact remains that the species found here is fairly distinct and is easily separated from the other species of the group.

Sepals and lateral petals green. Dorsal sepal bent forward over gynostegium. Lip curved 9-15 mm long, with longitudinal groove at the base; pattern gray to bluish, thin yellow edge.

Flowering time:
February-March

Habitat:
garigue, 0-1000 m

Occurrence:
common.

Ophrys iricolor *Desfontaines*

Rainbow Ophrys, Regenbogen Ragwurz
O. fusca ssp. *iricolor* Desfontaines

Sepals and lateral petals green, lip violet-black, underside reddish, 15-20mm long, about one and half times as long as that of *O. fusca* or *O. israelitica*, with blue iridescent pattern in the shape of two wings. Lip with longitudinal groove at the base. Lacks the thin yellow margin of *O. fusca*.

Flowering time:
February-March

Habitat:
garigue, on calcareous soils, 0-1000 m

Occurrence:
common.

Ophrys lutea *(Cav.)* ssp. **galilaea**
(H. Fleischm. et Bornm.) Soó

Yellow Ophrys, Gelbe Ragwurz
O. galilaea, O. sicula Tineo
O. lutea Cav. ssp. *murbeckii* (H. Fleischm.)Soó
O. lutea ssp. *minor* (Todaro) O. et E. Danesch

An orchid which is placed within the *fusca* complex of related species because it shares the common feature of the indentation at the top of the lip. It is easily recognised by the broad yellow margin to the lip, which is spread horizontally or is slightly upturned. A common plant in a variety of habitats, often preferring shady or damp terrain.

Flowering time:
February-April

Habitat:
garigue, maquis, pine
forest, 0-1000 m

Occurrence:
common.

Ophrys israelitica *Baumann et Künkele*

Omega Ophrys, Fleischmanns Ragwurz
O. fusca ssp. *fleischmannii*(Soó) Soó
O. fleischmannii (Hayek)
O. omegaifera ssp. *fleischmannii* (Hayek) Del Prete
O. omegaifera ssp. *israelitica*
(Baumann et Künkele) Morschek comb. nov.

Delforge reserves the name *O. omegaifera* ssp. *fleischmannii* or *O. fleischmannii* for the Cretan taxon, and *O. israelitica* for the taxon found in Cyprus. In *O. fleischmannii* the base of the lip bends upward whereas in *O. israelitica* it is flat.

Sepals and lateral petals green, dorsal sepal bending over gynostegium, lateral sepals spreading. Lip without longitudinal groove at the base, ground base colour dark brown with W-shaped white pattern.

Flowering time: February-March

Habitat: garigue, open pine forest, 100-1100 m

Occurrence: common.

105

The two related species characterised by very small petals.
They are easily recognised in the field using the lip shape
and pattern and the flowering time. The two plants remain
distinct and are treated at specific level.

Ophrys bornmuelleri *M. Schulze*

Bornmueller's Ophrys, Bornmuellers Ragwurz
O. bornmuelleri (M. Schulze ex Bomm.) ssp. *bornmuelleri*
O. fuciflora ssp. *bornmuelleri* (M. Schulze) B. et E. Willing
O. holoserica ssp. *bornmuelleri* (M. Schulze) Sundermann

Plant 20-40 cm tall. Sepals green or whitish, spreading,
dorsal sepal erect. Petals very small (ca 2 mm long)
whitish; lip 7-10 mm, entire with broad reddish or
yellowish hairy margin; edges spread or turned slightly
upward; appendage greenish, upturned; pattern on
lip variable.

Flowering time: late March-April

Habitat: garigue, often on reddish soils, 0-1000 m

Occurrence: locally common.

Ophrys levantina *Gölz et Reinhard*

Spider orchid
O. bornmuelleri ssp. *grandiflora* (H. Fleischm. et Soó)
O. fuciflora ssp. *bornmuelleri* var. *grandiflora*
(H. Fleischm. et Soó)

Plant 10-25 cm tall; sepals greenish white, often turned back, petals very small, pinkish. Lip entire with broad hairy margin, turned down; pattern variable, sometimes entirely absent. Flowers much earlier than *O. bornmuelleri*.

Flowering time:
February-March

Habitat:
garigue, often under bushes, 0-1000 m

Occurrence:
common.

Ophrys tenthredinifera *Willdenow*

Sawfly Ophrys, Wespen-Ragwurz

Sepals and lateral petals pink. Lip reddish-brown, rectangular, hairy. Edges spreading or turned down. Upturned appendage in central lower part of the lip.

Flowering time:
late February-early
March

Habitat:
garigue, 0-300 m

Occurrence:
very rare.

Ophrys apifera *Hudson*

Bee Orchid, Bienen-Ragwurz

Four varieties of *O. apifera* can be found on Cyprus, var. *apifera*, *bicolor*, *melena* and c*hlorantha*. These are identical in all respects except for flower colour. How is it that different populations of these varieties can coexist? The answer is that *O. apifera* is largely autogamous and therefore aberrant characters can easily establish themselves.

var. **apifera**: sepals pink to bright purple. Lip brown to purplish black, basafield orange to reddish-brown.

var. **bicolor***:* upper part of lip reddish-brown, lower part pale yellow.

var. **chlorantha**: sepals white or greenish-white, lip lemon-yellow.

var. **melena**: sepals pale pink, upper part of lip dark brown, lower part paler brown.

Plant to 50 cm high where it grows among tall reeds. The plant can be found in a variety of habitats from the edge of the Akrotiri salt lake to the igneous soils of Platres.

Flowering time: end March-May

Habitat: on a variety of soils, marshy meadows,

garigue, pine forest, 0-1100 m

Occurrence: locally common.

var. apifera

var. chlorantha

var. melena

var. bicolor

Ophrys argolica *H. Fleischm.* ssp. **elegans** *(Renz)*

Eyed Bee-Orchid, Argolis Ophrys, Zierliche Ragwurz
O. elegans (Renz)

A subspecies which occurs almost exclusively in Cyprus.
An early flowering orchid, to be found initially in flower on
the edge of the Akrotiri salt lake often hidden under cistus,
Pistacia lentiscus, cypressus and pine. Sepals pale pink,
strongly reflexed.

Flowering time:
mid January-March

Habitat:
garigue, maquis,
pine forest, 0-500 m

Occurrence:
locally common.

Someone looking at the Cypriot orchids belonging to the mammosa/sphegodes groups for the first time can be excused for feeling confused. There exists a bewildering variety of form and colour. How can this be explained? Cyprus appears to be the meeting point of species from the east and west, or is perhaps the birthplace of species that are now found elsewhere. So how can we describe what is found here? Even though there appears to be an endless variety of form one can pick out certain individuals that can be described as 'good species', i.e. species that are known from somewhere else, and describe the individuals that do not conform as being intermediate between the good species. The alternative approach would be to give entirely new names to the individuals that do not conform to the 'good species' thereby increasing the already burgeoning list of species found elsewhere.

Most Cypriot plants can be assigned to one of three species, *O. sintenisii, O. transhyrcana* or *O. mammosa.* Plants with an undivided lip to the flower, well developed basal swellings and strongly coloured lateral sepals are assigned to *O. mammosa;* plants with small basal swellings, weekly trilobed lip and greenish sepals are assigned to *O. sintenisii;* plants with a strongly trilobed lip and no basal swellings are assigned to *O. transhyrcana.*

O. sintenisii individuals tend to have yellowish/orange pigments whereas *O. mammosa* and *O. transhyrcana* individuals tend to have purple/dark-coloured pigments to the lip.

O. transhyrcana and *O. sintenisii* are usually synonymous in the literature, Delforge however treats both as distinct species (with some reservation) and this is the convention adopted here.

The alternetive approach is to admitt the presence of another species belonging to the sphegodes grouping, with an entire lip, no basal swellings, yellowish-orange pigments to the lip and green sepals. Such individuals occur in the area west of Cyprus, in Greece or the Aegean. Various species are suggested by different authors; Morschek suggests *O. aesculapi* but this is a plant of Northern Greece and unlikely to occur here. Delforge proposes *O. herae*, a plant of wider distribution in Greece and western Anatolia.

The question of the relationship of the Cypriot orchids with those of neighbouring countries looks like being settled only with the genetic techniques applied by Bateman et al as applied to the *Orchis / Neotinea / Aceras* genera.

To summarise; the characters that can be used to identify each species are sepal colouration, lip shape (trilobed/entire) and colour, the presence or absence of lateral protuberances and the length of the anther connective.

Ophrys sintenisii

Ophrys mammosa *Desfontaines*

Mammose Ophrys, Busen-Ragwurz
O. sphegodes Mill. ssp. *mammosa* (Desf.) Soó

Plant robust, to 60 cm high. Sepals green stained reddish-purple. Lip purplish brown, entire, lateral protuberances prominent up to 4 mm long. Basafield reddish brown, anther connective short, 1-2 mm long.

Flowering time: March-May

Habitat: garigue, abandoned vineyards, 100-1200 m

Occurrence: common.

Ophrys sphegodes *Mill* ssp. sphegodes *Erich Nelson*

Early Spider Ophrys, Spinnen-Ragwurz

One record of this plant, probably a misidentification

Ophrys mammosa

Ophrys sintenisii *H. Fleischmann et Bornmüller*

O. sphegodes ssp. *sintenisii* (H. Fleischm. et Bornm.) E. Nelson
O. sphegodes Mill. ssp. *transhyrcana* Cziernjakowska

Plant to 50 cm, sepals green, sometimes tinged red. Anther connective 2.0-2.5 mm long. It has a weakly-trilobed lip and small tubercles, although specimens with entire lips and no tubercles are found. It is in some ways intermediate in character between *O. mammosa* and *O. transhyrcana*. It flowers early, with *O. transhyrcana* starting in mid-January and is largely finished in the lowlands by the end of March.

Flowering time:
mid-January-April

Habitat:
garigue, abandoned vineyards,
100-1000 m

Occurrence:
common.

Ophrys transhyrcana Cziernjakowska

Kaspiche Ragwurz
O. sphegodes Mill. ssp. *transhyrcana* Cziernjakowska
O. sphegodes ssp. *sintenisii* (H. Fleischm. et Bomm.) E. Nelson

Sepals green, lower half of laterals stained reddish-purple.
Lip dark brown, sub-entire or three lobed, convex. Lateral
protuberances usually absent. Basafield dark brown, anther
connective 2-3.5 mm long.

Flowering time:
mid-January-April

Habitat:
garigue, abandoned
vineyards,
100-1000 m

Occurrence:
common.

The umbilicata and scolopax are related groups of species with authors placing species in these groups according to different criteria. Thus *O. lapethica* is usually placed in the *O. scolopax* and *O. kotschyi* in the *O. reinholdii* groups respectively. Delforge uses the chief criterion that species with the median sepal bending forward over the gynostegium are placed in the *O. umbilicata* group. So both *O. lapethica* and *O. kotschyi* fall within this group while *O. rhodia* does not.

Ophrys umbilicata and its subspecies appear in the literature under a plethora of synonyms. J. J .Wood in Meikle lists nine each for its two subspecies. Worse still, one man's variety or subspecies is another man's species with no agreement on the number and distribution of species in each area.

J.J. Wood (Meikle) recognises two subspecies, *Ophrys umbilicata* ssp. *umbilicata* and *Ophrys umbilicata* ssp. *attica f. flavomarginata.*

Delforge and Baumann & Künkele recognise three species, *O. umbilicata, O. flavomarginata,* and *O. rhodia.* A fourth species *O. attica* is also recognised as possibly occurring here.

Most specimens found in Cyprus will conform to either *O. umbilicata* or to *O. flavomarginata* (as well as to *O. kotschyi* and *O. lapethica*). A few (green sepals, dorsal sepal bending over the gynostegium, median lobe of lip convex with no yellowish margin) don't fall into either category and could be assigned to *O. attica.* The fourth species *O. rhodia* appears to be absent from Cyprus, although an odd specimen with a dorsal sepal bending back may be found-see photo.

The criteria for separating the different species are as follows:

Median sepal not bending forward
over the gynostegium .... **O. rhodia**
Median sepal bending forward
over the gynostegium

 Lip broadest in the middle .... **O. lapethica**
 Lip broadest at the apex

  Lip dark coloured with white markings . . **O. kotschyi**
  Lip not so

   Lip edges reflexed
   greenish yellow .... **O. flavomarginata**
   Lip edges bending under, not yellow

    Sepals: green .... **O. attica**
    Sepals: whitish or pink .... **O. umbilicata**

Ophrys kotschyi *H. Fleischmann et Soó*

Kotschy's Ophrys, Kotschys Ragwurz

One of the endemic orchids of Cyprus, it is certainly one of the most striking. The lip (12-18 mm) is about twice as long compared to say *O. umbilicata.* The pattern on the lip is variable and consists of a dark violet to almost black ground colour with white markings. The sepals are green, the dorsal sepal curving forward. Petals are dark green ca. 5 mm long and 2.5 mm wide.

Flowering time:
late February-March

Habitat:
garigue, abandoned
fields, 0-500 m

Occurrence:
locally common.

123

Ophrys lapethica *Gölz & Reinhard*

Woodcock Orchid, Schnepfen-Ragwurz
Ophrys scolopax Cavanilles

In Cyprus the nominate race *scolopax* is being given specific status and therefore considered an endemic under the name of *O. lapethica*. A common plant fairly well reported in the literature (J. J. Wood in Flora of Cyprus). At first glance it may appear similar to *O. umbilicata* however, it is always possible to separate the two.

Plant 10-40 cm high, sepals pale pink to purple violet, never white or green. Lip trilobed, convex, broadest at or just below the middle, unlike *O. umbilicata* where the lip is broadest towards the apex. Median sepal only slightly reflexed. Pattern extending only half-way down the lip.

Flowering time: February-March-beginning of April

Habitat: garigue, open woodland, 100-900 m

Occurrence: common.

Ophrys umbilicata *Desfontains*

Woodcock orchid, Nabel-Ragwurtz
O. umbilicata Desfontains ssp. *umbilicata*
O. scolopax Cav. ssp. *orientalis* (Renz)
O. orientalis (Renz) Soó
O. carmeli H. Fleischm. et Bornm. ssp. *orientalis* (Renz)

Plant 10-25 cm tall, sometimes many stems growing closely together. Sepals and lateral petals pink to greenish-white. Dorsal sepal bent over gynostegium. Lip trilobed, median lobe convex, broadest towards the apex.

Flowering time:
February-beginning
of April

Habitat:
garigue, 0-900 m

Occurrence:
common.

Ophrys attica *(Boiss. et Orphan.)* Soó *B. D. Jackson*

Mt. Carmel Ophrys, Attische Ragwurtz
O. carmeli ssp. *attica* (Boiss. et Orphan.) Renz
O. scolopax ssp. *attica* (Boiss. et Orpan.) E. Nelson
O. umbilicata ssp. *attica* (Boiss. et Orphan.) J.J. Wood

Plant 10-25 cm tall, sepals and lateral petals green, dorsal sepal bending over gynostegium. Lip trilobed, slim, edges bent under.

Flowering time:
January-beginning
of April

Habitat:
garigue, open forest,
0-300 m

Occurrence:
locally common.

Ophrys attica

Ophrys rhodia

129

Ophrys flavomarginata *(Renz)*
H. Baumann et Künkele

O. carmeli (non H. Fleischm. et Bornm.) E. Nelson
O. attika f. *flavomarginata* Renz

Plant 10-25 cm tall, sepals and lateral petals green, dorsal sepal bending over gynostegium. Lip trilobed with greenish yellow edge, broadest towards the apex.

Flowering time:
January-beginning
of April

Habitat:
garigue, open forest,
0-900 m

Occurrence:
common.

Dactylorhiza romana
D. sulphurea ssp. *pseudosambucina*
D. sambucina ssp. *pseudosambucina*

Orchis laxiflora *O. laxiflora* ssp. *laxiflora*

Orchis morio ssp. syriaca *O. syriaca, O. morio* ssp. *libani*

Orchis palustris *O. laxiflora* ssp. *palustris*

Ophrys argolica ssp. elegans *O. elegans*

Ophrys bornmuelleri *O. bornmuelleri* ssp. *bornmuelleri*
O. fuciflora ssp. *bornmuelleri, O. holoserica* ssp.
bornmuelleri

Ophrys flavomarginata/attica
O. umbilicata ssp. *attica f. flavomarginata,*
O. carmeli ssp. *attica*

Ophrys fusca ssp. fusca *O. fusca, O. funerea*

Oprhys iricolor *O. fusca* ssp. *iricolor*

Ophrys israelitica
O. fusca ssp. *fleischmannii, O. omegaifera* ssp. *israelitica*
O. omegaifera ssp. *fleischmannii, O. fleischmannii*

Ophrys levantina *O. bornmuelleri* ssp. *grandiflora*
O. fuciflora ssp. *bornmuelleri* var. *grandiflora*

Ophrys lutea ssp. galilaea *O. galilaea,*
O. lutea ssp. *murbeckii*

Ophrys mammosa   *O. sphegodes* ssp. *mammosa*

Ophrys transhyrcana/sintenisii
O. sphegodes ssp. *transhyrcana, O. sintenisii,*
O. sphegodes ssp. *sintenisii*

Ophrys scolopax *O. lapethica*

Ophrys umbilicata   *O. umbilicata* ssp. *umbilicata,*
O. scolopax ssp. *orientalis, O. carmeli* ssp. *orientalis*

A b b r e v i a t i o n s

cm   centimeter
m   meter
mm   millimeter
sp.   species (singular)
spp.   species (plural)
ssp.   subspecies
syn.   synonym
var.   variety

G l o s s a r y

apochromic	colour variant, lacking in pigment
autogamous	self fertilising
basafield	area of lip above the speculum
calcareous	chalk, limestone, rich in calcium carbonate
column	the flower structure formed by the fusion of the style, the stigma and the stamens
connective	part of anther between the two pollen sacks
endemic	found only in a particular region
epichile	front part of the lip
galea	hood formed by sepals in *Serapias*
garigue	vegetation characteristic of Mediterranean with low-growing shrubs
gynostegium	the organ forming the column bearing the male and female parts
hybrid	a cross between two species
hypochile	rear part of the lip
igneous	of volcanic or magmatic origin
labellum/lip	lowermost of three petals, usually highly differentiated from the others
maquis	vegetation characteristic of Mediterranean with tall-growing shrubs
petal	inner part of the perianth
perianth	sepals and petals
pollinia	mass of pollen grains
sepal	external part of the perianth
stamen	the male part of the flower
speculum	central part of lip, sometimes H-shaped, or reduced to two dots
tepal	name used for sepals and petals when similar
viscidium	sticky disc at base of pollinia which attaches them to a visiting insect

Baumann H., Künkele S., **Die wildwachsenden Orchideen Europas**, Kosmos-Verlag 1982

Blamey M., Grey-Wilson C., **Mediterranean Wild Flowers**, HarperCollins 1993, ISNB 0 00 219901 7

Briggs D., Walters S. M., **Plant Variation and Evolution**, World University Library

Butler K. P., **Field Guide to the Orchids of Britain and Europe**, Crowood Press, 1991

Delforge P., **Orchids of Britain and Europe**, Collins Photo Guide, 1995

Davies P.& J. and Huxley A., **Wild orchids of Britain and Europe**, The Hogarth Press, 1988

Georgiades C., **Orchids of Cyprus,** 1998, ISBN 9963-7540-5-8

Gould S. J., **Ever since Darwin**, Penguin

Hansen, K.& R., Rückbrodt, U. & D., Kreutz, C. A. J., (1990), **Beitrag zur Kenntnis und Verbreitung der Orchideenflora von Zypern mit Interims-Verbreitungsskarten**. Mitt. BL. Arbeitskr. Heim. Orch. Baden-Württ. **22** (1):73-171/1990

Meikle R. D., **Flora of Cyprus** vol. 1 and vol. 2. Kew.

Morschek G.& K., **Orchids of Cyprus**, ISNB 3-00-000956-6

Pantelas V., Papachristoforou T., Christodoulou P., **The Endemics**, 1993, ISBN 9963-7931-0-X

The endemic plants of Cyprus, Bank of Cyprus publication 1995, ISBN 9963-42-052-4

Flowering times	Jan.	Feb.	Mar.	April	May
Anacamptis pyramidalis			—		
Barlia robertiana		——			
Dactylorhiza romana		—	—		
Neotinea maculata			——	——	—
Ophrys apifera			——	——	—
argolica ssp. elegans		——			
bornmuelleri			——	——	
attica/flavomarginata		——	—		
fusca		——	—		
iricolor			——		
israelitica		—	—		
kotschyi		—	—		
lapethica			——		
levantina		——	—		
lutea ssp. galilaea		——	——		
mammosa		——			
sintenisii		—	——		
tenthredinifera			——		
transhyrcana		——			
umbilicata			——		
Orchis anatolica			——		
anatolica ssp. troodi			——		
collina		——			
coriophora ssp. fragrans				——	—
italica			——	——	
laxiflora				——	—
palustris					——
punctulata			——	——	
quadripunctata		——	——		
sancta				——	—
simia				——	
syriaca		——	——		
Platanthera chlorantha					——
Serapias all species				——	—

136

Flowering times	June	July	Aug	Nov/Dec
Cephalanthera rubra	——	——		
Dactylorhiza iberica	——	——		
Epipactis				
veratrifolia	——	——		
troodi	——	——		
microphylla	—			
condensata		——		
Limodorum abortivum	—			
Neotinea maculata				
Platanthera chlorantha ssp. holmboei	——	—		
Spiranthes spiralis				——

		Akrotiri		Aphames	
Anacamptis	pyramidalis	x		x	
Barlia	robertiana			x	
Dactylorhiza	romana				
Neotinea	maculata			x	
Ophrys	apifera	x		x	
argolica ssp. elegans		x			
	bornmuelleri	x		x	
	fusca	x		x	
flavomarginata/attica		x		x	
	iricolor	x		x	
	israelitica	x		x	
	kotschyi	x			
	lapethica	x		x	
	levantina	x		x	
lutea ssp. galilaea		x		x	
	mammosa	x		x	
transhyrcana/sintenisii		x		x	
	umbilicata	x		x	
Orchis	collina	x		x	
coriophora ssp. fragrans		x		x	
	italica	x		x	
	laxiflora			x	
	palustris	x			
	punctulata				
	quadripunctata			x	
	sancta	x		x	
	simia			x	
	syriaca	x		x	
Serapias	laxiflora	x		x	
orientalis/parviflora		x			
	vomeracea	x		x	
Spiranthes	spiralis	x			

138

		Akamas	
Anacamptis	pyramidalis	x	
Barlia	robertiana	x	
Dactylorhiza	romana	x	
Neotinea	maculata	x	
Ophrys	apifera	x	
argolica ssp. elegans		x	
	bornmuelleri	x	
	fusca	x	
flavomarginata/attica		x	
	iricolor	x	
	israelitica	x	
	kotschyi	x	
	lapethica	x	
	levantina	x	
lutea ssp. galilaea		x	
	mammosa	x	
transhyrcana/sintenisii		x	
	tenthredinifera	x	
	umbilicata	x	
Orchis	anatolica ssp. troodi	x	
	collina	x	
coriophora ssp. fragrans		x	
	italica	x	
	laxiflora	x	
	punctulata	x	
	quadripunctata	x	
	sancta	x	
	syriaca	x	
Serapias	laxiflora	x	
orientalis/parviflora		x	
	vomeracea	x	
Spiranthes	spiralis	x	

139

		Platres		Troodos	
Barlia	robertiana	x			
Cephalanthera	rubra			x	
Dactylorhiza	romana	x			
	iberica			x	
Epipactis	veratrifolia	x		x	
	troodi	x		x	
	microphylla				
	condensata			x	
Limodorum	abortivum	x		x	
Neotinea	maculata	x		x	
Ophrys	apifera	x			
	mammosa	x			
	israelitica	x			
	sintenisii	x			
Orchis					
anatolica ssp. troodi		x		x	
coriophora ssp. fragrans					
Platanthera	chlorantha	x		x	
	ssp. holmboei				
Serapias	laxiflora	x			

140

N o t e s

Anacamptis pyramidalis		
Barlia robertiana		
Cephalanthera rubra		
Dactylorhiza romana		
Dactylorhiza iberica		
Epipactis veratrifolia		
Epipactis troodi		
Epipactis microphylla		
Epipactis condensata		
Limodorum abortivum		
Neotinea maculata		

Ophrys apifera		
Ophrys argolica ssp. elegans		
Ophrys attica		
Ophrys bornmuelleri		
Ophrys flavomarginata		
Ophrys fusca		
Ophrys israelitica		
Ophrys iricolor		
Ophrys kotschyi		
Ophrys lapethica		
Ophrys levantina		
Ophrys lutea ssp. galilaea		
Ophrys mammosa		
Ophrys sintenisii		
Ophrys tenthredinifera		
Ophrys transhyrcana		
Ophrys umbilicata		

C h e c k l i s t

Orchis anatolica		
Orchis anatolica ssp. troodi		
Orchis collina		
Orchis coriophora ssp. fragrans		
Orchis italica		
Orchis laxiflora		
Orchis syriaca		
Orchis palustris		
Orchis punctulata		
Orchis quadripunctata		
Orchis sancta		
Orchis simia		
Orchis tridentata		

Platanthera chlorantha ssp. holmboei		
Spiranthes spiralis		
Serapias laxiflora		
Serapias levantina		
Serapias orientalis		
Serapias parviflora		
Serapias vomeracea		

Index to the English names

page